Friends Make the World BETTER!

by Taylor Conner and Kendall Conner

Illustrated by Friends

TO: RJ and walker

FROM: Addie

You are special! 😊

ISBN: 979-8-218-01809-2

Cover Art: Watercolor by Kendall Conner
Special thanks to Kenya Newman for her assistance
with the digital design.

To our village of doctors, researchers, therapists, teachers, family, and friends:

Thank you for your encouragement and support, prayers, and helping to advance our efforts to find a cure for Leigh Syndrome! We believe that together we can move mountains!

-T.C and K.C.

Friends come in all shapes, colors, and sizes,
so please step up when the opportunity arises.

When you meet someone new, always say "hello!"
You may be surprised how that kindness can grow.

If you invite a friend to join you in a game,
always make an effort to ask them their name.

Celebrate differences and find common ground,
and you just might find a friend coming around.

Pay close attention to the words that they say,
good friends have a way of making your day!

They will compliment you on what you wear,
even if you have crazy rainbow-colored hair!

Sometimes friends might say, "I believe in you!"
And this encouragement will help get you through.

Even in the hardest of times when everything goes wrong,
a true friend will remind you that you're capable and strong.

If you slip and take a fall,
a friend will help you through it all.

Friends are people that you can trust,
and having them by your side is a must.

For when you encounter a big bully at school,
a friend will speak up and say "that's not cool."

When you are feeling sad and blue,
a friend will always be there for you.

Good friends are always helpful and kind,
and offer a hand when you're in a bind.

Even if you haven't seen them in a while,
a friend has a way of making you smile.

Some will be besties or that special one,
but lots of friends make life sweet and fun!

If you have a disagreement with one of your friends,
it's important to act quickly and try to make amends.

You may be at a loss or unaware,
but asking questions shows you care.

By now, you know that friendships are a two-way street, and relationships like these will make your life complete.

Making friends is not hard to do,
just remember it all starts with YOU!

Made in the USA
Columbia, SC
10 August 2022

65017524R10015